This is a big jam bun.

It is in the sun.

Look at the jam.

See it run.

Jelly licks it.

Yum, yum, yum.

Jelly eats the big jam bun.

She is full.

She cannot run.

Jelly sits in the sun,
full of jam and full of
bun.

This is a plum jam bun.

It is in the sun.

Look at the jam.

See it run.

Bean licks it.

Yum, yum, plum.

Bean eats the plum
jam bun.
Yum, yum, yum.
It fills his tum.

He is full.

He cannot run.

He sits with Jelly in the sun.